CHECK YOUR
VOCABULARY FOR
MEDICINE

a workbook for users

second edition

Original material by
David Riley

Edited and revised by
Liz Greasby

PETER COLLIN PUBLISHING

First published in Great Britain 1995
Second edition published 2000

Published by Peter Collin Publishing Ltd
1 Cambridge Road, Teddington, Middx, UK

© Peter Collin Publishing Ltd 1995, 2000

British Library Cataloguing in Publication Data
A catalogue record for this book is available from the British Library

ISBN 1-901659-47-X

Text typeset by PCP Ltd
Printed by Nuffield Press, Oxfordshire, UK

Workbook Series

Check your:

Vocabulary for Banking and Finance	0-948549-96-3
Vocabulary for Business, 2nd edition	1-901659-27-5
Vocabulary for Colloquial English	0-948549-97-1
Vocabulary for Computing, 2nd edition	1-901659-28-3
Vocabulary for English	1-901659-11-9
Vocabulary for Hotels, Tourism, Catering	0-948549-75-0
Vocabulary for Law, 2nd edition	1-901659-21-6
Vocabulary for Marketing	1-901659-48-8
Vocabulary for Medicine, 2nd edition	1-901659-47-X

Specialist English Dictionaries

English Dictionary for Students	1-901659-06-2
Dictionary of Accounting	0-948549-27-0
Dictionary of Agriculture, 2nd edition	0-948549-78-5
Dictionary of American Business	0-948549-11-4
Dictionary of Automobile Engineering	0-948549-66-1
Dictionary of Banking & Finance	0-948549-12-2
Dictionary of Business, 2nd edition	0-948549-51-3
Dictionary of Computing, 3rd edition	1-901659-04-6
Dictionary of Ecology & Environment, 3rd edition	0-948549-74-2
Dictionary of Government & Politics, 2nd edition	0-948549-89-0
Dictionary of Hotels, Tourism, Catering	0-948549-40-8
Dictionary of Human Resources, 2nd edition	0-948549-79-3
Dictionary of Information Technology, 2nd edition	0-948549-88-2
Dictionary of Law, 3rd edition	1-901659-43-7
Dictionary of Library & Information Management	0-948549-68-8
Dictionary of Marketing, 2nd edition	0-948549-73-4
Dictionary of Medicine, 3rd edition	1-901659-45-3
Dictionary of Printing & Publishing, 2nd edition	0-948549-99-8
Dictionary of Science & Technology	0-948549-67-X

For details about our range of English and bilingual dictionaries and workbooks, please contact:

Peter Collin Publishing
1 Cambridge Road, Teddington, TW11 8DT, UK
tel: (+44) 020 8943 3386   fax: (+44) 020 8943 1673   email: info@petercollin.com
web site: **www.petercollin.com**

Introduction

The worksheets in this workbook contain a variety of exercises appropriate for students requiring a working knowledge of English medical terminology. The worksheets can be used either for self-study or in the classroom and can be completed in any order. Several have 'extensions': short classroom exercises based on the language in the main exercise. All the questions within this workbook are based on the Peter Collin Publishing *Dictionary of Medicine, third edition* (ISBN 1-901659-45-3).

This workbook is aimed at students with at least an intermediate level of English. However, many people who work in medicine have to read in English on a regular basis; students with a more basic level of English may therefore already have the passive vocabulary to handle many of the exercises.

Specialist vocabulary

It is important to appreciate that 'knowing' specialist vocabulary involves more than simply recognising it.

- You can understand the meaning of a word when reading or listening and yet be unable to remember that same word when speaking or writing.
- You may remember the word, but use it incorrectly. This can be a grammatical problem, like knowing that 'fracture' can be used both as a noun and as a verb. Or it may be a question of collocation: a surgeon *makes an incision* during an operation, but when he wants a piece of bread he simply *cuts* it.
- Then there is the question of the sound of the word. Can you pronounce it? And do you recognise it when you hear it pronounced?

For these reasons - memory, use and sound - it is important that students practise specialist vocabulary so that they can learn to use it more confidently and effectively. The exercises in this workbook will help students to expand their knowledge and use of medical vocabulary.

Photocopiable material

All the worksheets can be legally photocopied to use in class. If, as a teacher, you intend to use most of the book with a class you may find it more convenient for the students to buy a copy each. You are not allowed to photocopy or reproduce the front or back cover.

Using the *Dictionary of Medicine*

All of the vocabulary taught or practised in this workbook is in the Peter Collin Publishing *Dictionary of Medicine*. The *Dictionary of Medicine* gives definitions in simple English which students can read and understand. Many of the examples and definitions in the workbook are taken directly from the dictionary. Students should have a copy of the *Dictionary of Medicine* for referring to when completing the exercises; using the dictionary is an essential part of successful language learning.

Structure of a *Dictionary of Medicine* entry

Each entry within the dictionary includes key elements that help a student understand the definition of the term and how to use it in context. Each term has a clear example, and part of speech. This is followed by example sentences and quotations from newspapers and magazines that show how the term is used in real life. These elements of the dictionary are used to create the questions within this workbook.

Vocabulary Record Sheet

At the back of the book is a Vocabulary Record Sheet. Recording useful vocabulary in a methodical way plays a key role in language learning and could be done, for example, at the end of each lesson. The *Dictionary of Medicine* is a useful tool for ensuring that the personal vocabulary record is accurate and is a good source for example sentences to show how words are used, as well as for notes about meaning and pronunciation, etc.

Workbook contents

Using the workbook

Most students find it easier to assimilate new vocabulary if the words are learned in related groups, rather than in isolation. For example, words frequently occur in the same context as their opposites and, as such, it makes sense to learn the pairs of opposites together (*see worksheets on pages 7 and 29*). Similarly, mind maps encourage students to look for connections between words (*see worksheet on page 9*). The exercises and activities in this workbook have all been grouped into sections. These sections practise different elements of medical vocabulary, enabling the student to gain a fuller understanding of the words learnt.

The first section, **Word-building** (*pages 1-9*), encourages the student to identify links between words and to learn words that are morphologically related (for example, verbs and nouns which have the same stems). Within the **Parts of Speech** (*pages 10-20*) section, the emphasis is on understanding meanings and how to use terms in their correct grammatical forms. The worksheets in the third section practise the **Pronunciation** of medical vocabulary (*pages 21-24*). The section **Vocabulary in Context** (*pages 25-36*) includes topic-specific exercises such as identifying diseases and illnesses from their descriptions. The activities in the last section, **Puzzles & Quizzes** (*pages 37-49*), expand students' knowledge and use of vocabulary in a fun way.

Communicative crosswords

Included in the last section are three communicative crosswords. These are speaking exercises where students complete a half-finished crossword by exchanging clues with a partner. There are two versions of the crossword: A & B. The words which are missing from A are in B, and vice versa. No clues are provided: the students' task is to invent them. This is an excellent exercise for developing linguistic resourcefulness; in having to define words themselves, students practise both their medical vocabulary and the important skill of paraphrasing something when they do not know the word for it.

Using Communicative crosswords

Stage 1 – Set-up. Divide the class into two groups - A and B - with up to four students in each group. Give out the crossword: sheet A to group A, sheet B to group B together with a copy of the *Dictionary of Medicine*. Go through the rules with them. Some answers may consist of more than one word.

Stage 2 - Preparation. The students discuss the words in their groups, exchanging information about the words they know and checking words they do not know in the *Dictionary of Medicine*. Circulate, helping with any problems. This is an important stage: some of the vocabulary in the crosswords is quite difficult.

Stage 3 - Activity. Put the students in pairs - one from group A and one from group B. The students help each other to complete the crosswords by giving each other clues.
Make sure students are aware that the idea is to help each other complete the crossword, rather than to produce obscure and difficult clues.

- What's one down?
- *It's a person who works in a hospital.*
- A doctor?
- *A sort of doctor. He does operations.*
- A surgeon?
- *Yes, that's right.*

| A A | B B |
| A A | B B |

Students work in groups, checking vocabulary

Alternatively, students can work in small groups, each group consisting of two As and two Bs and using the following strategies:

i)	defining the word
ii)	describing what the item looks like
iii)	stating what the item is used for
iv)	describing the person's role
v)	stating what the opposite of the word is
vi)	giving examples
vii)	leaving a gap in a sentence for the word
viii)	stating what the word sounds like.

A B	A B
A B	A B

Students work in pairs, co-operating to solve their crosswords

Word association 1: missing links

Each of the sets of four words below can be linked by one other word. All the words are related to medical matters. What are the missing words? Write them in the centre of the charts.

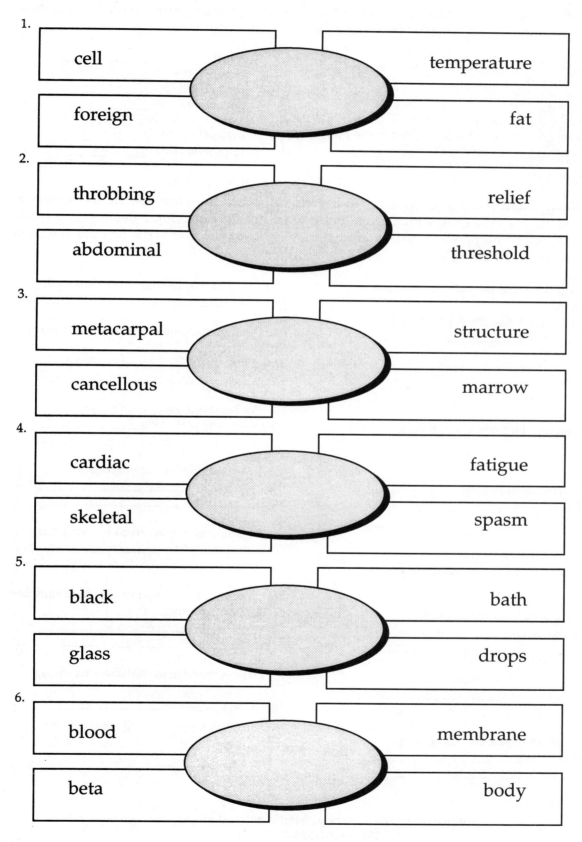

1.
cell — temperature
foreign — fat

2.
throbbing — relief
abdominal — threshold

3.
metacarpal — structure
cancellous — marrow

4.
cardiac — fatigue
skeletal — spasm

5.
black — bath
glass — drops

6.
blood — membrane
beta — body

Based on the **Dictionary of Medicine**, third edition
ISBN 1-901659-45-3
© Peter Collin Publishing Ltd

Word formation: nouns

A fast way to expand your vocabulary is to make sure you know the different forms of the words you learn.

Exercise 1. The words in this list are all verbs. What are the noun forms? Write them in the second column. The first one has been done for you as an example.

1. diagnose _____diagnosis_____
2. examine _____
3. prescribe _____
4. suffer _____
5. operate _____
6. cure _____
7. recover _____
8. analyse _____

9. infect _____
10. experience _____
11. replace _____
12. degenerate _____
13. refer _____
14. exceed _____
15. withdraw _____

Exercise 2. First, check your answers to Exercise 1 in the key. Then rewrite the sentences below, changing the verbs (which are in **bold**) to nouns. Do not change the meaning of the sentences, but be prepared to make grammatical changes if necessary. The first one has been done for you as an example.

1. I **diagnosed** that the patient had a heart condition.
My diagnosis was that the patient had a heart condition.

2. I **examined** the patient fully.
I made a full_____

3. I **prescribed** a course of antibiotics.
I wrote a_____

4. He **suffered** very little.
He experienced very little_____

5. We **operated** immediately.
The_____

6. This disease cannot be **cured**.
There is no_____

7. He has **recovered** fully.
He has made a full_____

8. The lab **analysed** the blood sample.
The lab made an_____

9. We found that the tissue was **infected**.
We found an_____

10. He has **experienced** six years of tropical work.
He has six years'_____

11. We **replaced** the patient's hip.
The patient was given a hip_____

12. His condition has **degenerated**.
There has been a _____

13. The patient was **referred** to a specialist.
The patient was given a_____

14. The amount of sugar in the blood sample **exceeded** the norm.
There was an_____

15. This is the time to **withdraw** the drugs treatment.
This is the time for the_____

2   Based on the **Dictionary of Medicine**, third edition
ISBN 1-901659-45-3
© Peter Collin Publishing Ltd

Two-word expressions

Make 15 two-word expressions connected with medicine by combining words from the two lists: A and B. Match each expression with the appropriate phrase. Use each word once. The first one has been done for you as an example.

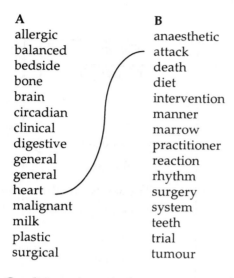

A	B
allergic	anaesthetic
balanced	attack
bedside	death
bone	diet
brain	intervention
circadian	manner
clinical	marrow
digestive	practitioner
general	reaction
general	rhythm
heart	surgery
malignant	system
milk	teeth
plastic	trial
surgical	tumour

1. Condition where the heart suffers from defective blood supply because one of the arteries becomes blocked by a blood clot.
   heart attack

2. Substance given to make a patient lose consciousness so that a major surgical operation can be carried out.
   _____

3. Soft tissue in cancellous bone.
   _____

4. Treatment of illness by surgery.
   _____

5. A child's first twenty teeth, which are gradually replaced by permanent teeth.
   _____

6. Surgery which repairs defective or deformed parts of the body.
   _____

7. Condition where the nerves in the brain stem have died, and the patient can be certified as dead, although the heart may not have stopped beating.
   _____

8. Way in which a doctor behaves towards a patient (or a patient who is in bed).
   _____

9. Effect (such as a skin rash or sneezing) produced by a substance to which a person has an allergy.
   _____

10. Trial carried out in a medical laboratory on a patient or on tissue from a patient.
    _____

11. Cancer, a tumour which is cancerous and can reappear or spread into other tissue, even if removed surgically.
    _____

12. Doctor who treats many patients in a district for all types of illness, though not specializing in any one branch of medicine.
    _____

13. Rhythm of daily activities and bodily processes frequently controlled by hormones, which repeats every 24 hours.
    _____

14. All the organs in the body that are associated with the digestion of food.
    _____

15. Diet that provides all the nutrients needed in the correct proportions.
    _____

Based on the **Dictionary of Medicine**, third edition
ISBN 1-901659-45-3
© Peter Collin Publishing Ltd

Plural formation

In *Column A* of this table there are 25 nouns relating to medicine. For each of the nouns decide whether the correct plural form is in *Column B* or *Column C* and then circle it.

The first question has been done for you as an example.

	Column A	Column B	Column C
1.	stratum	stratums	(strata)
2.	foot	foots	feet
3.	fibula	fibulae	fibulas
4.	glomerulus	glomerulae	glomeruli
5.	abscess	abscesses	abscessi
6.	joint	jointes	joints
7.	bulla	bullae	bullas
8.	testis	testises	testes
9.	septum	septa	septums
10.	fossa	fossas	fossae
11.	crisis	crises	crisises
12.	humerus	humeruses	humeri
13.	syringe	syringes	syringae
14.	acetabulum	acetabula	acetabulums
15.	larva	larvae	larvi
16.	chorda	chordas	chordae
17.	varix	varices	varixi
18.	fungus	fungi	funguses
19.	ganglion	ganglions	ganglia
20.	villus	villi	villae
21.	atrium	atria	atriums
22.	pons	pontes	ponses
23.	ovum	ovums	ova
24.	bout	bouts	boutae
25.	cortex	cortexes	cortices

Based on the **Dictionary of Medicine**, third edition
ISBN 1-901659-45-3
© Peter Collin Publishing Ltd

Word formation: adjectives

The italicised words in the sentences in Column A are all nouns. What are the adjective forms? Complete the sentences in Column B using the correct adjective forms.

	Column A	Column B
1.	The surgeons operated to repair the *defect* on the patient's heart valve.	The surgeons operated to repair the patient's …
2.	His diet has a calcium *deficiency*.	His diet is calcium-…
3.	She has a physical *dependence* on amphetamines.	She is physically …
4.	The doctor noted an *excess* of bile in the patient's blood.	The doctor noted an …
5.	An attack of *hypoglycaemia* can be prevented by eating glucose or a lump of sugar when feeling faint.	A …
6.	The vaccine should give *immunity* to tuberculosis.	The vaccine should make you …
7.	They have periods of complete *inactivity*.	They have periods when they are completely …
8.	The *pain* in his foot is so great that he can hardly walk.	His foot is so …
9.	I injured my *spine* in the crash.	I suffered …
10.	She complained of *stiffness* in the joints.	She complained of …

Based on the **Dictionary of Medicine**, third edition
ISBN 1-901659-45-3
© Peter Collin Publishing Ltd

Word association 2: partnerships

Exercise 1.

Link each *verb* on the left with a *noun* on the right to make 10 'partnerships'. The first one has been done for you as an example.

Verbs		Nouns
1.	administer	an improvement
2.	analyse	a baby
3.	arrange	antibiotics
4.	burp	the treatment
5.	catch	your arms
6.	detect	an appointment
7.	discontinue	a sample
8.	ease	the pain
9.	fold	a drug
10.	prescribe	a cold

Exercise 2.

Complete these sentences using the partnerships from Exercise 1. You may have to make some changes to fit the grammar of the sentences. The first one has been done for you as an example.

1. The doctor will __administer a drug__ to the patient.

2. She was _____ .

3. As soon as the patient reported severe side-effects, the doctor decided to _____ .

4. I've _____ from one of my colleagues at work.

5. The laboratory _____ of the food and found traces of bacteria.

6. He sat down and _____ .

7. I would like to _____ with the dental hygienist for 10.00am tomorrow.

8. She had an injection to _____ in her leg.

9. The health visitor advised the new parents to _____ after feeding.

10. The nurses _____ in the patient's condition.

Based on the **Dictionary of Medicine**, third edition
ISBN 1-901659-45-3

Opposites 1: prefixes

Exercise 1.

English often uses prefixes to create opposites. There are several different prefixes that are used. Choose the right prefix for each of the adjectives below and write them into the table. The first one has been done for you:

active adequate boiled capable compatible complete

conscious correct curable direct fertile fit healthy hygienic legal movable palpable

pasteurized pure qualified reducible regular sanitary soluble stable well

il-	im-	in-	ir-	un-
1.	1.	1. inactive	1.	1.
	2.	2.	2.	2.
	3.	3.		3.
		4.		4.
		5.		5.
		6.		6.
		7.		7.
		8.		8.
		9.		9.
		10.		
		11.		

Exercise 2.

Use ten of the adjectives in the table to complete these sentences. The first one has been done for you as an example.

1. He was found ___unconscious___ in the street.

2. He felt _____ and had to go home.

3. She is _____ of feeding herself.

4. The children have a very _____ diet.

5. The nurse noted that the patient had developed an _____ pulse.

6. She used to play a lot of tennis, but she became _____ in the winter.

7. _____ milk can carry bacilli.

8. Cholera spread rapidly because of the _____ conditions in the town.

9. The patient was showing signs of an _____ mental condition.

10. He is suffering from an _____ disease of the blood.

Extension. Work with a partner and test each other. One partner closes the book, while the other asks questions such as *"What's the opposite of conscious?"*.

Based on the **Dictionary of Medicine**, third edition
ISBN 1-901659-45-3
© Peter Collin Publishing Ltd

Word formation: verbs

Exercise 1.
The words listed in the table below are nouns. What are the verb forms of these nouns? The first question has been done for you as an example.

1. abuse	*abuse*	16. perspiration	
2. admission		17. preparation	
3. bandage		18. provision	
4. breath		19. reabsorption	
5. castration		20. regeneration	
6. consultation		21. registration	
7. convalescence		22. regurgitation	
8. conversion		23. rehabilitation	
9. fertilization		24. reproduction	
10. immmunization		25. resuscitation	
11. implant		26. sedation	
12. insurance		27. stammer	
13. maceration		28. stitch	
14. management		29. suppression	
15. occurrence		30. sweat	

Exercise 2.
Choose ten verbs from Exercise 1 and write a sentence below for each one. Write the correct form of each verb in the column on the right and leave gaps for the verbs in the sentences. Cover up the right-hand column and give the sentences to another student as a test. For example:

She .... with her local GP.	*registered*

1. ....
2. ....
3. ....
4. ....
5. ....
6. ....
7. ....
8. ....
9. ....
10. ....

Based on the **Dictionary of Medicine**, third edition
ISBN 1-901659-45-3
© Peter Collin Publishing Ltd

Word association 3: mind maps

A mind map is a way of organising vocabulary to show the connections between words. This mind map is based on the word 'surgery'.

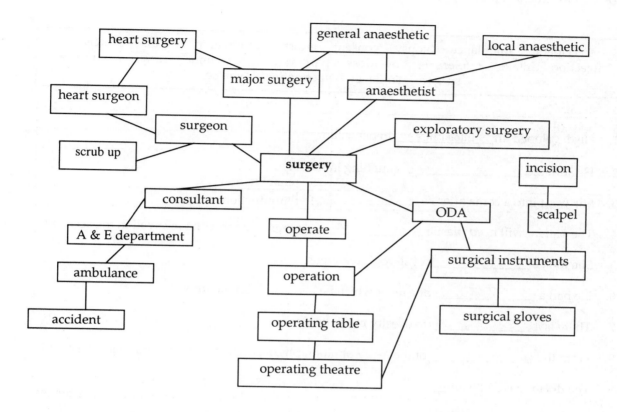

Exercise 1.
Find words and expressions in the mind map that fit the following definitions.

1. Special room in a hospital where surgeons carry out operations ....
2. Nurse working in the operating department ....
3. Department in a hospital which deals with accident and emergency cases ....
4. Surgical operations involving important organs in the body ....
5. Doctor who specializes in surgery ....
6. Substance which removes the feeling in a certain part of the body only ....
7. Senior specialized doctor in a hospital ....
8. Surgical operation to remedy a condition of the heart ....
9. To wash the hands and arms carefully before an operation ....
10. Surgical intervention or act of cutting open a patient's body to treat a disease or disorder ....

Exercise 2.
Design a mind map for one or more of the following:
*   health
*   hospital
*   patient

Based on the **Dictionary of Medicine**, third edition
ISBN 1-901659-45-3
© Peter Collin Publishing Ltd

Nouns

There are 20 nouns connected with medicine in the box below. Use them to complete the sentences — in some cases you will need to make them plural. The first one has been done for you as an example.

accident	ambulance	biopsy	consent	effort	examination	excess	exercise
injection	intake	~~intolerance~~	overdose	paroxysm	programme	rash	recurrence
	surgery	tendency	vaccination	whisper			

1. He developed an ___intolerance___ to penicillin.

2. He suffered _____ of coughing in the night.

3. She went into a coma after an _____ of heroin.

4. The patient will need plastic _____ to remove the scars he received in the accident.

5. She took a _____ of steroid treatment.

6. He had a _____ of a fever which he had caught in the tropics.

7. There is a _____ to obesity in her family.

8. From the _____ of the X-ray photographs, it seems that the tumour has not spread.

9. The doctor gave him an _____ to relieve the pain.

10. He doesn't take enough _____: that's why he's fat.

11. The injured man was taken away in an _____.

12. She was advised to reduce her _____ of sugar.

13. The _____ of the tissue from the growth showed that it was benign.

14. The parents gave their _____ for their son's heart to be used in the transplant operation.

15. She has a sore throat and can only speak in a _____.

16. It took a lot of _____ to walk even this short distance.

17. Her body could not cope with an _____ of blood sugar.

18. Three people were injured in the _____ on the motorway.

19. _____ is mainly given against cholera, diphtheria, rabies, smallpox, tuberculosis and typhoid.

20. She had a high temperature and then broke out in a _____ .

Based on the **Dictionary of Medicine**, third edition
ISBN 1-901659-45-3
© Peter Collin Publishing Ltd

Adjectives 1

Complete the sentences using the adjectives in the box. Use each adjective once only. The first one has been done for you as an example.

bitter	compatible	confused	delicate	highly-strung	hoarse	hygienic
inactive	inadequate	inborn	inoperable	insanitary	invisible	left-handed
motionless	poisonous	predisposed	regular	~~safe~~	severe	

1. This is a ___**safe**___ painkiller, with no harmful side-effects.

2. Some mushrooms are good to eat and some are _____ .

3. The surgeons are trying to find a donor with a _____ blood group.

4. The surgeon decided that the cancer was _____ .

5. _____ people need special scissors.

6. The body has an _____ tendency to reject transplanted organs.

7. The hospital has _____ staff to deal with a major accident.

8. The serum makes the poison _____ .

9. A _____ outbreak of whooping cough occurred during the winter.

10. Old people can easily become _____ if they are moved from their homes.

11. Catatonic patients can sit _____ for hours.

12. Don't touch food with dirty hands: it isn't _____.

13. All the members of the family are _____ to vascular diseases.

14. Oranges are sweet, but quinine is _____.

15. The bones of a baby's skull are very _____.

16. Cholera spread rapidly because of the _____ conditions in the town.

17. She is _____, so don't make any comments about her appearance, or she will burst into tears.

18. He was advised to make _____ visits to the dentist.

19. The microbes are _____ to the naked eye, but can clearly be seen under a microscope.

20. He became _____ after shouting too much.

Based on the **Dictionary of Medicine**, third edition
ISBN 1-901659-45-3
© Peter Collin Publishing Ltd

Adjectives 2

Complete the sentences using the adjectives in the box. Use each adjective once only. The first one has been done for you as an example.

awkward	bedridden	crippled	deaf	exhausted	forbidden	infirm
inflamed	lame	~~lethal~~	level	obsessive	painful	persistent	premature
	severed	subjective	tender	viable	depressed	

1. These fumes are _____lethal_____ if inhaled.

2. He was _____ in a car crash.

3. She suffered from a _____ cough.

4. The psychiatrist gave a _____ opinion on the patient's problem.

5. My grandfather is quite _____ now.

6. The skin has become _____ around the sore.

7. Her temperature has remained _____ for the last hour.

8. His foot is so _____ he can hardly walk.

9. A foetus is _____ by about the 28th week of the pregnancy.

10. You have to speak slowly and clearly when you speak to Mr Jones because he's quite _____ .

11. The baby was born five weeks _____ .

12. The patient was _____ after the second operation.

13. The tumour is in an _____ position for surgery.

14. He is _____ and has to be looked after by a nurse.

15. He has been _____ since damaging his leg in the accident.

16. He has an _____ desire to steal small objects.

17. Her shoulders are still _____ where she got sunburnt.

18. Surgeons tried to sew the _____ finger back onto the patient's hand.

19. She was _____ for weeks after the death of her husband.

20. Smoking is _____ in the cinema.

Based on the **Dictionary of Medicine**, third edition
ISBN 1-901659-45-3
© Peter Collin Publishing Ltd

Verbs 1

The sentences in **Column A** contain examples of useful verbs in medicine. In **Column B** **there** are definitions of the verbs. Read the examples and match the verbs (in *italics*) with the definitions. Then write the infinitive forms into the spaces in the definitions in **Column B**. The first one has been done for you as an example.

Column A: Examples	Column B: Definitions
1. After the accident the passengers were *treated* in hospital for cuts.	a) <u>diagnose</u> means to identify a patient's condition or illness, by examining the patient and noting symptoms
2. He *depends on* drugs to relieve the pain.	b) _____ means to look after a sick or injured person or to try to cure a sick person
3. He *specializes in* children with breathing problems.	c) _____ means to make a patient healthy
4. She *suffers* from headaches.	d) _____ means to put at risk
5. She was *vaccinated* against smallpox as a child.	e) _____ means to give instructions for a patient to get a certain dosage of a drug or a certain form of therapeutic treatment
6. Some forms of cancer cannot be *cured*.	f) _____ means to study or treat one particular disease or one particular type of patient
7. The calamine lotion will *soothe* the rash.	g) _____ means to have an illness for a long period of time
8. The doctor *diagnosed* appendicitis.	h) _____ means to treat a patient's condition by cutting open the body and removing a part which is diseased or repairing a part which is not functioning properly
9. The doctor *prescribed* a course of antibiotics.	i) _____ means to use a vaccine to give a person immunization against a specific disease
10. The drug *suppresses* the body's natural instinct to reject the transplanted tissue.	j) _____ means to relieve pain
11. The operation may *endanger* the life of the patient.	k) _____ means to rely on something
12. The surgeons decided to *operate* as the only way of saving the baby's life.	l) _____ means to remove (a symptom) or to reduce the action of something completely or to stop (the release of a hormone)

Based on the **Dictionary of Medicine**, third edition
ISBN 1-901659-45-3
© Peter Collin Publishing Ltd

Verbs 2

The sentences in **Column A** contain examples of useful verbs in medicine. In **Column B** there are definitions of the verbs. Read the examples and match the verbs (in *italics*) with the definitions. Then write the infinitive forms into the spaces in the definitions in **Column B**. The first one has been done for you as an example.

Column A: Examples	Column B: Definitions
1. He was *admitted* this morning.	a) _____ means to pass from one place to another
2. The cancer is not *responding* to drugs.	b) _____ means to damage or to hurt
3. Their diet *lacks* essential proteins.	c) _____ means to go through or into something
4. The doctors *saved* the little boy from dying of cancer.	d) _____ means to make a hole through something
5. The end of the broken bone has *penetrated* the liver.	e) _____ means to investigate the inside of something
6. The new heart has *performed* very well.	f) _____ means to rescue someone or to stop someone from being hurt or killed
7. The patient was *transferred* to a special unit.	g) _____ means not to have enough of something
8. She *fainted* when she saw the blood.	h) __admit__ means to register a patient in a hospital
9. The surgeon *probed* the wound with a scalpel.	i) _____ means to stop something happening
10. Walking to work every day won't *harm* you.	j) _____ means to react to something or to begin to get better because of a treatment
11. The treatment is given to *prevent* the patient's condition from getting worse.	k) _____ means to lose consciousness or to stop being conscious for a short time
12. The ulcer *perforated* the duodenum.	l) _____ means to work or to do

Based on the **Dictionary of Medicine**, third edition
ISBN 1-901659-45-3

Verbs: past tense ~ regular verbs

All the verbs in the box relate to medical matters. Use the past tense forms to complete the sentences. The first question has been done for you as an example.

adapt aggravate develop examine faint fracture prolong react ~~receive~~ recover require strain suffer tremble weigh

1. He __received__ a new kidney from his brother.

2. He _____ his back lifting the table.

3. She _____ from her concussion in a few days.

4. It was so hot standing in the sun that he _____ .

5. The doctors decided that her condition _____ surgery.

6. She _____ from poor circulation, which made her feel the cold.

7. She _____ well to her new diet.

8. The embryo _____ quite normally in spite of the mother's illness.

9. His tibia _____ in two places.

10. The patient _____ badly to the penicillin

11. The nurse _____ the baby on the scales.

12. The treatment _____ her life by three years.

13. Playing football only _____ his knee injury.

14. The doctor _____ the boy's throat.

15. His hands _____ with the cold.

Based on the **Dictionary of Medicine**, third edition
ISBN 1-901659-45-3
© Peter Collin Publishing Ltd

Verbs: mixed tenses

All the verbs in the box relate to medical matters. Use them to complete the sentences. **You may have to change the forms of the verbs to fit the grammar of the sentences. (Remember the five forms of English verbs - for example: take, takes, took, taken, taking.)** The first question has been done for you as an example.

beat	bite	break	burn	control	expel	experience	heal	kick	measure	
	observe	overcome	progress	rebuild	undergo	~~visit~~				

1. I am going to ___visit___ my brother in hospital.

2. She _____ her disabilities and now leads a normal life.

3. After the accident her pelvis was completely _____.

4. She has _____ several operations.

5. He is _____ pains in his right upper leg.

6. She fell off a wall and _____ her leg.

7. A thermometer _____ temperature.

8. Air is _____ from the lungs when a person breathes out.

9. She could feel the baby _____ .

10. A minor cut will _____ faster if it is left without a bandage.

11. The girl _____ her hand on a hot frying pan.

12. He _____ his asthma with a bronchodilator.

13. My heart was _____ fast.

14. She was _____ by an insect.

15. The doctor asked how the patient was _____ .

Based on the **Dictionary of Medicine**, third edition
ISBN 1-901659-45-3
© Peter Collin Publishing Ltd

Phrasal verbs

Natural English conversation includes many phrasal verbs. These are verbs made up of two words: a verb and a preposition. For example: 'I *get up* at eight o'clock'. Complete the sentences below using the phrasal verbs in the box. You will have to change the forms of some of the verbs to make the grammar of the sentence correct. The first one has been done for you as an example.

1. He __*got over*__ his cold.

2. The nurses are _____ her very well.

3. He must have _____ the disease when he was travelling in Africa.

4. She often _____ in front of the TV.

5. The boy was _____ by a car.

6. She _____ and cried as she described the symptoms to the doctor.

7. He _____ his father.

8. The doctor asked him to _____ his shirt.

9. He was _____ mucus.

10. The blood transfusion service _____ a large number of donors.

11. I was advised to _____ smoking.

12. He was _____ by a blow on the head.

13. The nurse _____ the patient with pillows.

14. My uncle is _____ and he is quite deaf.

15. The new surgeon will _____ the operation.

Phrasal verbs
break down = to collapse in a nervous state
bring up = to cough up material such as mucus from the lungs or throat
carry out = to perform
depend on = to rely on something
drop off = to fall asleep
get on = to become old
~~*get over*~~ = to become better after an illness
give up = not to do something any more
knock down = to make something fall down by hitting it hard
knock out = to hit someone so hard that he is no longer conscious
look after = to take care of
pick up = to catch a disease
prop up = to support a patient
take after = to be like (a parent)
take off = to remove (especially clothes)

Extension. Work with a partner: write a dialogue which includes at least seven of the phrasal verbs from this page.

Based on the **Dictionary of Medicine**, third edition
ISBN 1-901659-45-3
© Peter Collin Publishing Ltd

Verbs: active/passive

Change the sentences below from active to passive tense. For example:

Active: *The GP referred the patient to a consultant.*
Passive: *The patient was referred to a consultant by the GP.*

Remember that it is not always necessary to mention the subject in a passive sentence. For example:

Active: *We have identified the cause of this outbreak of dysentery.*
Passive: *The cause of this outbreak of dysentery has been identified.*

1. The nurse noticed an acceleration in the patient's pulse rate.
    Passive:...

2. The consultant is allowing him to watch the operation.
    Passive:...

3. All chemists sell the tablets.
    Passive:...

4. The doctor diagnosed appendicitis.
    Passive:...

5. The paramedics comforted the injured person until the ambulance arrived.
    Passive:...

6. The midwife delivered the twins.
    Passive:...

7. The gland was producing an excess of hormones.
    Passive:...

8. They looked after him very well in hospital.
    Passive:...

9. We examined the tissue under the microscope.
    Passive:...

10. The doctor gave me an unpleasant mixture to drink.
    Passive:...

11. You cannot take the lotion orally.
    Passive:...

12. Toxic fumes poisoned the workers.
    Passive:...

13. Doctors are predicting a rise in cases of whooping cough.
    Passive:...

14. The drug suppresses the body's natural instinct to reject the transplanted tissue.
    Passive:...

Based on the **Dictionary of Medicine**, third edition
ISBN 1-901659-45-3
© Peter Collin Publishing Ltd

Adverbs

The sentences below do not read correctly. Identify the adverbs in the sentences and then swap the adverbs around so that each sentence makes sense.

Some of the adverbs could be used in several of the sentences.

1. The bandage was medicinally tied around her wrist.
   ....

2. Immediately, she is very advanced for her age.
   ....

3. If the patient sweats fairly, it may be necessary to cool his body with cold compresses.
   ....

4. The tumour is excessively placed and not easy to reach.
   ....

5. She manages all her patients very mentally.
   ....

6. The relief team loosely requires more medical supplies.
   ....

7. This is a physically antiseptic solution.
   ....

8. Mildly he is very weak, but his mind is still alert.
   ....

9. He became ill efficiently after he came back from holiday.
   ....

10. The herb can be used awkwardly.
    ....

11. He has been working as a doctor only for a severely short time.
    ....

12. Her breathing was urgently affected.
    ....

Prepositions

The sentences in this exercise contain **mistakes**. The mistakes are all in the prepositions and there are three types:

1.	missing preposition	I spoke ^him about this last week. *to*
2.	wrong preposition	We're meeting again in ^Tuesday. *on*
3.	unnecessary preposition	I'll telephone to you tomorrow.

Find the mistakes and correct them.

1. The hospital has installed new apparatus through the physiotherapy department.

2. Her lips were cracked of the cold.

3. The boy's little toe was crushed the door.

4. The tissue was examined on the microscope.

5. It is important that needles used at injections should be sterilized.

6. He is recovering from a bout flu.

7. She was given to a pain-killing injection.

8. Some types of wool can irritate to the skin.

9. This report quotes the number of cases of cervical cancer from thousand patients tested.

10. The doctor put the patient to sleep within a strong narcotic.

11. She burnt her hand at the hot frying pan.

12. We have no spare beds on the hospital at the moment.

13. He will have an operation to remove of an ingrowing toenail.

14. Please ensure that the patient takes of his medicine.

Based on the **Dictionary of Medicine**, third edition
ISBN 1-901659-45-3
© Peter Collin Publishing Ltd

Word stress 1

One of the keys to English pronunciation is *stress* - emphasis. There are three possible patterns for three-syllable words:

A: ■□□   **hos**-pi-tal
B: □■□   pre-**scrip**-tion
C: □□■   rec-om-**mend**

Read these four conversations. Find all the three-syllable words and classify them by their pronunciation. There are 27 in total. Put them in the correct sections of the table on the right. The first one has been done for you as an example.

Dialogue 1

● When was she <u>admitted</u> to hospital?
○ At about four o'clock.
● Has there been any improvement?
○ No, her condition is stable. We're waiting to see how things develop.

Dialogue 2

● What do you recommend?
○ Well, first of all: cut down on fatty foods.
● And what else?
○ Take regular exercise, don't smoke and keep alcohol down to a minimum.

Dialogue 3

● What's the problem?
○ I went to give him his injection and I saw that he'd started to haemorrhage.
● We'll have to operate. Make sure all the equipment is prepared.
○ I'll go down to the theatre and check.

Dialogue 4

● So, is it serious?
○ Don't worry. It's probably just an allergic reaction.
● Are you just saying that to reassure me?
○ You're fine. Look, I'm going to give you a prescription for some painkillers…

Dialogue 5

● Have you got the test results yet?
○ Well, they're still incomplete, but it's clear that it's positive.
● Any idea when infection took place?
○ I'd say five or six weeks ago, but that's just an opinion. Do you want to see her medical history?

Group A: ■□□
1
2
3
4
5
6
7
8
9
10
11
12
13
Group B: □■□
1 **admitted**
2
3
4
5
6
7
8
9
10
11
Group C: □□■
1
2
3

Extension. Practise the dialogues with a partner.

Based on the **Dictionary of Medicine**, third edition
ISBN 1-901659-45-3
© Peter Collin Publishing Ltd

Word stress 2

One of the keys to English pronunciation is *stress* - emphasis. There are three normal patterns for four-syllable words:

A: ■□□□ **vac**-ci-na-ted   B: □■□□ pneu-**mo**-ni-a   C: □□■□ in-flu-**en**-za

Exercise 1. Complete the sentences below using the four-syllable words in the table. The first question has been done for you as an example.

1. She appeared to be improving, but a _**complication**_ set in and she died a few hours later.

2. Bell's Palsy causes facial _____ .

3. Come right now: it's an _____!

4. The patient was having difficulties breathing so we put him on a _____.

5. She had an _____ to replace the cornea.

6. He was given a general _____ before the surgeons began work.

7. As a precaution against AIDS we use _____ needles.

8. He can't take aspirin: he has an _____ to it.

9. Rub your hands together to get the _____ going.

10. He couldn't _____ the movements of his arms and legs.

11. An _____ was organised to test the drug on a small group of people.

12. Tests confirmed the _____ of the growth.

13. This is the allergen which was _____ for the patient's reaction.

14. _____ showed that the food contained bacteria.

15. The surgeons are trying to find a _____ donor.

16. A diet high in _____ fats increases the risk of heart disease.

17. The surgeon _____ to the students how to make the incision.

18. As many as 60-70% of diarrhoeal deaths are caused by _____.

19. Autistic children do not _____ with anyone.

20. _____ is a common antibiotic produced from a fungus.

Exercise 2. Decide which pronunciation pattern is correct for each of the words in the table and tick the appropriate column

	A ■□□□	B □■□□	C □□■□
anaesthetic			
analysis			
circulation			
communicate			
compatible			
complication			
coordinate			
dehydration			
demonstrated			
disposable			
emergency			
experiment			
independent			
intolerance			
malignancy			
operation			
paralysis			
penicillin			
respirator			
responsible			
saturated			

Based on the **Dictionary of Medicine**, third edition
ISBN 1-901659-45-3
© Peter Collin Publishing Ltd

Present simple

Verbs in the present tense add an 's' in the third person singular: I work, you work, he/she/it works. But the 's' has three different pronunciations. Look at these examples:

A: /s/, for example *treats*
B: /z/, for example *heals*
C: /ɪz/, for example *changes*

Find the third person present tense verbs in these sentences and classify them by their pronunciation. Put them in the correct columns in the table on the right. Be careful: some sentences have more than one example. There are 27 verbs in total. The first one has been completed for you as an example.

1. The patient ~~breathes~~ with difficulty and coughs and sneezes constantly.

2. This drug helps to alleviate the symptoms and reduces the risk of reinfection.

3. A person whose resistance is low catches diseases more easily.

4. When someone panics his heart beats more rapidly and his temperature rises.

5. The laboratory analyses the blood samples and then the doctor examines the results and diagnoses the condition.

6. He then recommends a course of treatment and prescribes any necessary drugs.

7. This drug relaxes the muscles and relieves pain.

8. The gland releases hormones into the bloodstream, causing an immediate reaction.

9. If the patient sleeps well, he wakes feeling refreshed.

10. She suffers constant pain and controls it by using morphine.

11. This treatment counteracts the effects of the infection.

12. It is a procedure which cures the condition or kills the patient.

13. If the surgeon operates now the chance of success increases to about 50%.

14. The sinoatrial node regulates the heart beat.

Group A: /s/
1. ....
2. ....
3. ....
4. ....
5. ....
6. ....
7. ....
8. ....
9. ....

Group B: /z/
1. ....**breathes**..............
2. ....
3. ....
4. ....
5. ....
6. ....
7. ....
8. ....
9. ....

Group C: /ɪz/
1. ....
2. ....
3. ....
4. ....
5. ....
6. ....
7. ....
8. ....
9. ....

Extension. The same rule applies to plural nouns: /s/ patients, /z/ doctors, /ɪz/ nurses. Work with a partner and find five example nouns for each sound.

Based on the **Dictionary of Medicine**, third edition
ISBN 1-901659-45-3
© Peter Collin Publishing Ltd

Past tense

Regular verbs have three different pronunciations in the past tense (or the past participle). The difference is in the sound you use for the ending. Look at these examples:

A: /t/, for example *plac**ed***
B: /d/, for example *examin**ed***
C: /ɪd/, for example *inject**ed***

Find the past tense verbs in these sentences and classify them by their pronunciation. Put them in the correct columns in the table on the right. Be careful: some sentences have more than one verb. There are 23 examples in total. The first one has been done for you as an example.

1. She was ~~vaccinated~~ against smallpox as a child.

2. The doctor diagnosed him as having hepatitis B.

3. Her condition improved, so we reduced the dose.

4. He consulted a specialist, who recommended surgery.

5. The patient coughed and sneezed all through the consultation.

6. The surgeons replaced her hip with a metal one.

7. The doctor prescribed a course of antibiotics.

8. The doctor's speedy action prevented further complications.

9. The pharmacist mixed the chemicals in this bottle.

10. The surgeons operated immediately on the child.

11. He was completely cured.

12. The nurse disinfected and dressed the wound.

13. She was treated by a heart specialist.

14. His pulse rate increased by 10%.

15. The attack was preceded by a rise in body temperature.

16. The surgical instruments were sterilized before use.

17. Nobody noticed that the patient's blood pressure had dropped.

18. The surgeon probed the wound with a scalpel.

Group A: /t/
1..
2..
3..
4..
5..
6..
7..
8..

Group B: /d/
1..
2..
3..
4..
5..
6..
7..

Group C: /ɪd/
1.....vaccinated.................
2..
3..
4..
5..
6..
7..
8..

Based on the **Dictionary of Medicine**, third edition
ISBN 1-901659-45-3
© Peter Collin Publishing Ltd

Good advice

These sentences all give very good advice, but they have been divided into separate halves. Match the half-sentences in Column A with the half-sentences in Column B to make 14 sentences which are correct, complete and true.

Column A	Column B
1. Regular exercise is ...	a) ... burn easily in the sun.
2. A balanced diet should ...	b) ... cause back pain.
3. Medicines should ...	c) ... be inoculated against diphtheria.
4. A patient in shock should ...	d) ... be kept out of the reach of children.
5. Not taking any exercise is ...	e) ... be kept warm and lying down.
6. Reading in bad light can ...	f) ... about 2.5 litres of fluid each day.
7. A hard bed is good ...	g) ... good for the heart.
8. A normal adult should drink ...	h) ... for someone with back problems.
9. HIV can be transmitted ...	i) ... be sterilized before use.
10. Bad posture can ...	j) ... make the eyes ache.
11. People with fair complexions ...	k) ... provide all the nutrients needed, in the correct proportions.
12. Surgical instruments must ...	l) ... an unhealthy way of living.
13. Babies should ...	m) ... be by pressure and elevation.
14. Haemorrhage control routinely should ...	n) ... by using non-sterile needles.

Extension. Working with a partner, write five pieces of medical advice.

Based on the **Dictionary of Medicine**, third edition
ISBN 1-901659-45-3
© Peter Collin Publishing Ltd

Multiple meanings

Some words have more than one meaning. For example, the word *pulse* means the pressure wave in an artery when the heart beats, but it also refers to a certain type of vegetable: beans and peas. In the table below 19 meanings appear in the column on the left. Match each meaning to one of the seven words across the top. The first one has been done for you as an example.

	cold	degree	fit	light	notice	patient	turn
1. A person who is in hospital or who is being treated by a doctor.							
2. To attach an appliance correctly, e.g. an artificial hand.							
3. A unit of measurement.							
4. To see or take note of.							
5. To change into something different.							
6. Not heavy.							
7. An illness, with inflammation of the nasal passages, in which the patient sneezes or coughs and has a blocked and running nose.							
8. The level of how important or serious something is.							
9. To move the head or body to face in another direction.							
10. Being able to wait a long time without getting annoyed							
11. A piece of writing giving information, usually put in a place where everyone can see it.							
12. To be the right size or shape.							
13. A slight illness or an attack of dizziness.							
14. A sudden attack of a disorder, e.g. epilepsy.							
15. A thing which shines and helps one to see.							
16. A title given by a university or college to a person who has successfully completed a course of studies.							
17. Strong and physically healthy.							
18. Not warm or hot.							
19. Nearer white in colour than black.							

Based on the **Dictionary of Medicine**, third edition
ISBN 1-901659-45-3
© Peter Collin Publishing Ltd

Odd one out

In each set of words one is the *odd one out*: different from the others. Find the word that is different, and circle it.

For example:

o   callosum...................   cerebellum.................   colliculus.................   (coccyx)...................

Coccyx is the odd one out. It is a bone; the others are all parts of the brain.

1	aching...................	bleeding..................	nagging...................	throbbing...................
2	hand...................	kidney...................	leg...................	liver...................
3	ankle...................	elbow...................	knee...................	forearm...................
4	ear...................	eye...................	face...................	nose...................
5	nurse...................	orderly...................	surgeon...................	patient...................
6	bandage...................	forceps...................	probe...................	scalpel...................
7	expiration...................	inspiration...................	respiration...................	supination...................
8	cataracts...................	eyelids...................	nearsightedness........	strabismus...................
9	improve...................	get better...................	recover...................	relapse...................
10	iris...................	lens...................	palm...................	pupil...................
11	oval window............	semicircular canals...	tympanic membrane	vertebral column......
12	copper...................	iron...................	nickel...................	zinc...................
13	break...................	crack...................	fracture...................	wound...................
14	metacarpal bone.......	nasal bone................	occipital bone..........	zygomatic arch.........
15	liver...................	heart...................	pancreas...................	spleen...................
16	bite...................	chew...................	swallow...................	taste...................
17	hepatalgia.............	hernia................	liver...................	hepatocyte............
18	epidermis.............	pore...................	dermis................	diabetes................

Based on the **Dictionary of Medicine**, third edition
ISBN 1-901659-45-3
© Peter Collin Publishing Ltd

Body parts - categories

In this table there are 38 words for parts of the body and six categories. Decide which category or categories each part belongs to. The first one has been done for you as an example.

	arm	hand	leg	foot	torso	head
abdomen					x	
Achilles tendon						
ankle						
buttock						
calf						
chest						
chin						
ear						
elbow						
eye						
eyebrow						
eyelash						
eyelid						
finger						
forearm						
forehead						
gum						
hip						
knee						
knuckle						
lip						
nail						
navel						
neck						
nipple						
nose						
palm						
rib						
scalp						
shoulder						
sole						
temple						
thigh						
thumb						
toe						
tongue						
tooth						
wrist						

Based on the **Dictionary of Medicine**, third edition
ISBN 1-901659-45-3

Opposites 2

Exercise 1.
Match the words in *italics* with their opposites in the box on the right. The first one has been done for you as an example.

1. The opposite of *back* is ......front...........................
2. The opposite of *acute* is ....
3. The opposite of *dead* is ....
4. The opposite of *improve* is ....
5. The opposite of *healthy* is ....
6. The opposite of *open* is ....
7. The opposite of *major* is ....
8. The opposite of *reduce* is ....
9. The opposite of *smooth* is ....
10. The opposite of *benign* is ....

alive
chronic
closed
deteriorate
~~front~~
ill
increase
malignant
minor
rough

Exercise 2.
Complete these sentences using the words from Exercise 1. Use one word from each pair of opposites.

1. She had an _____ attack of shingles.
2. He became excited, causing his pulse rate to _____.
3. He was very ill, but now his condition has begun to _____.
4. The calf muscles are at the _____ of the lower leg.
5. She put cream on her hands, which were _____ from heavy work.
6. The tumour is _____ and so may reappear even if removed surgically.
7. The hospital is _____ to visitors from noon to five o'clock.
8. The doctor arrived too late: the patient was already _____ .
9. There's nothing wrong with you: you're completely _____.
10. He had to undergo _____ surgery on his heart.

Extension. Work with a partner and test each other. One partner closes the book, while the other asks questions such as *"What's the opposite of back?"*.

Based on the **Dictionary of Medicine**, third edition
ISBN 1-901659-45-3
© Peter Collin Publishing Ltd

Abbreviations

Test your medical abbreviations. What do the following stand for? Check the ones you don't know in the dictionary. The first one has been done for you as an example.

1. A & E ....Accident & Emergency...

2. AIDS ....

3. BMR ....

4. CAT ....

5. CHD ....

6. D & V ....

7. DOA ....

8. GP ....

9. HAV ....

10. HIV ....

11. MD ....

12. OTC ....

13. PM ....

14. PMA ....

15. PMT ....

16. RQ ....

17. RSI ....

18. SAD ....

19. SIDS ....

20. STD ....

21. TB ....

22. TBI ....

23. UV ....

24. VDH ....

25. WHO ....

Extension. Work with a partner and test each other. One partner closes the book, while the other asks questions such as *"What does A & E stand for?"*.

Based on the **Dictionary of Medicine**, third edition
ISBN 1-901659-45-3
© Peter Collin Publishing Ltd

Symptoms & common illnesses 1

These words are all used to talk about illnesses: their symptoms and effects. Tick the ones you understand. Check the others in the dictionary.

1. allergic reaction	6. inflammation	11. runny nose
2. blister	7. itchy	12. sneeze
3. cough	8. malformation	13. spot
4. fever	9. rash	14. malaise
5. infectious	10. resistance	15. swelling

Read the descriptions below and match them to the names of the illnesses in the box on the right.

1. An infectious disease of the upper respiratory tract, with fever, malaise and muscular aches. It is transmitted by a virus and occurs in epidemics.
....

2. A common infectious viral disease of children, with mild fever, swollen lymph nodes and a rash. It can cause stillbirth or malformation of an unborn baby if the mother catches the disease while pregnant.
....

allergic rhinitis
coryza
infectious parotitis
influenza
pertussis
rubella
rubeola
varicella

3. An illness, with inflammation of the nasal passages, in which the patient sneezes and coughs and has a blocked and running nose.
....

4. An infectious disease of children, caused by a herpes virus, and characterized by fever and red spots which turn to itchy blisters.
....

5. An infectious disease of children where the body is covered with a red rash. It can weaken the body's resistance to other disease, especially bronchitis and ear infections. If caught by an adult it can be very serious.
....

6. An infectious disease of children, with fever and swellings in the salivary glands, caused by a paramyxovirus.
....

7. An infectious disease affecting the bronchial tubes. It is common in children and sometimes very serious. The patient coughs very badly and makes a characteristic 'whoop' when inhaling after a coughing fit.
....

8. An inflammation in the nasal passage and eyes. It is caused by an allergic reaction to flowers, their pollen and scent, as well as to dust.
....

Based on the **Dictionary of Medicine**, third edition
ISBN 1-901659-45-3
© Peter Collin Publishing Ltd

Symptoms & common illnesses 2

Exercise 1.
Many illnesses also have informal names. Match the informal and formal names listed below. The first one has been done for you as an example.

INFORMAL	FORMAL
1. Chickenpox is the same as	allergic rhinitis
2. A cold is the same as	infectious parotitis
3. The flu is the same as	coryza
4. German measles is the same as	influenza
5. Hay fever is the same as	rubella
6. Measles is the same as	rubeola
7. Mumps is the same as	pertussis
8. Whooping cough is the same as	varicella

Exercise 2.
Complete these six conversations between doctors and patients by writing in the name of the illness. Use the informal terms from the table above.

1. What seems to be the trouble?
   My eyes and my nose are running all the time.
   I feel terrible.
   When did this begin?
   At the beginning of July.
   It's probably just ....

2. What's the problem?
   It's my son. He's got a rash and swelling in his armpits.
   Does he have a fever?
   Yes.
   Hmm. He may have..........................

3. How are you feeling?
   I've got this terrible cough.
   Mm-hmm.
   And after I cough I make a noise when I try to breathe.
   Sounds like ....

4. How are you today?
   Oh, not very well. I've got a cough and a terrible cold.
   Do you have a fever?
   Umm, yes I do.
   It's probably a touch of ....

5. What's the problem?
   It's my daughter. She's got a fever and this swelling.
   Where's the swelling?
   In her throat.
   It could be...

6. So, what can I do for you?
   It's the twins. They're covered in these dreadful red spots.
   Are they experiencing any itching?
   Yes, they are.
   It may be..

Extension. Practise the conversations with a partner.

Based on the **Dictionary of Medicine**, third edition
ISBN 1-901659-45-3
© Peter Collin Publishing Ltd

Diagnosis

Read the eleven descriptions which follow, using your dictionary as and when necessary. What is the disease or illness being described in each case?

1. A disorder of the nervous system in which there are convulsions and loss of consciousness due to disordered discharge of cerebral neurons.

    ....

2. A condition where tissues die and decay as a result of bacterial action because the blood supply has been lost through injury or disease of the artery.

    ....

3. A condition where the lens of the eye gradually becomes hard and opaque.

    ....

4. A slow, progressive disorder of elderly people, it affects the parts of the brain which control movement. The symptoms include trembling of the limbs, a shuffling walk and difficulty in speaking.

    ....

5. An infectious disease in which infected lumps form in the tissue. Its commonest form is infection of the lungs, causing patients to lose weight, cough blood and have a fever. It is caught by breathing in germs or by eating contaminated food, especially unpasteurized milk.

    ....

6. A hereditary disease of the pancreas or mucoviscidosis, in which there is a malfunction of the exocrine glands. Symptoms include loss of weight, abnormal faeces and bronchitis. If diagnosed early, it can be controlled with vitamins, physiotherapy and pancreatic enzymes.

    ....

7. Serious bacterial disease spread through food or water. The infected person suffers from diarrhoea, cramp in the intestines and dehydration. The disease is often fatal.

    ....

8. A serious, infectious disease of children. Its first symptoms are a sore throat, followed by a slight fever, rapid pulse and swelling of the glands in the neck. A fibrous growth like a membrane forms in the throat and can close the air passages. The disease is often fatal, either because the patient is asphyxiated or because the heart becomes fatally weakened.

    ....

9. A disorder of the brain, mainly due to brain damage occurring before birth or due to lack of oxygen during birth. The patient may have bad coordination of muscular movements, impaired speech, hearing and sight, and sometimes mental retardation.

    ....

10. Inflammation of the membrane lining the intestines and the stomach, caused by a viral infection, and resulting in diarrhoea and vomiting.

    ....

Extension. Write a description of a disease or illness and see if your partner can recognize it.

How it works

Match the half-sentences in column A with the half-sentences in column B to make 18 sentences which are correct, complete and true. The first one has been done for you as an example.

Column A	Column B
1. Fluid accumulates in the tissue …	a) … the acetabulum at the hip and the tibia at the knee.
2. The autonomic nervous system works …	b) …the chest muscles relax and the lungs become smaller.
3. Cartilage is thick connective tissue which …	c) … as a man grows older.
4. A blood vessel is any tube (artery, vein, capillary) that …	d) … of patients suffering from dropsy.
5. The pituitary gland secretes hormones that …	e) … according to the ABO system
6. The femur joins …	f) … deoxygenated blood from the heart to the lungs for oxygenation.
7. Expiration takes place when …	g) … lines the joints and acts as a cushion.
8. The pulmonary arteries take …	h) … to digest fatty substances and to neutralize acids.
9. The trachea runs …	i) … is about 72 beats a minute.
10. Bile is produced by the liver, stored in the gall bladder and used …	j) … derived from the carotid artery.
11. The colon is divided …	k) … when a person is asleep or even unconscious.
12. Holocrine glands …	l) … to human life.
13. The prostate gland tends to enlarge …	m) … carries blood round the body.
14. The very high frequency waves of ultrasound …	n) … from the larynx to the lungs.
15. Oxygen is essential …	o) … can be used to detect and record organs or growths inside the body.
16. The supply of blood to the sublingual region is …	p) … into four distinct sections.
17. The normal adult pulse …	q) … are secretory only.
18. Blood groups may be classified …	r) …. control the functioning of the other glands.

Based on the **Dictionary of Medicine**, third edition
ISBN 1-901659-45-3
© Peter Collin Publishing Ltd

Instruments and equipment

Match each of the following instruments and items of equipment with its correct description below. The first one has been done for you as an example.

bandage catheter curette drain forceps gag hook pipette probe scalpel
sling splint stethoscope stretcher syringe thermometer tourniquet ~~wheelchair~~

1. __wheelchair__ = a chair with wheels in which an invalid can sit and move around

2. _____ = a small, sharp, pointed knife used in surgery

3. _____ = an instrument used to explore inside a cavity or wound

4. _____ = an instrument similar to a pair of scissors, used for holding and pulling

5. _____ = an instrument like a long thin spoon, used for scraping the inside of an organ

6. _____ = a thin glass tube used for taking and measuring samples of liquid

7. _____ = a device used to constrict an artery and reduce the flow of blood

8. _____ = an instrument with a bent end, used for holding structures apart in operations

9. _____ = a tube used to remove liquid from the body or the site of an operation

10. _____ = an instrument which is placed between a patient's teeth to stop him closing his mouth

11. _____ = a tube with a plunger which slides down inside it, forcing the contents out through a needle, or slides up the tube, allowing a liquid to be sucked into it

12. _____ = a tube which is passed into the body along one of the passages

13. _____ = a piece of cloth which is wrapped around a wound or an injured limb

14. _____ = a triangular bandage attached around the neck, used to support an injured arm and prevent it from moving

15. _____ = a folding bed, with handles, on which an injured person can be carried by two people

16. _____ = a stiff support attached to a limb to prevent a broken bone from moving

17. _____ = two earpieces connected to a tube and a metal disc, used to listen to sounds made inside the body

18. _____ = an instrument for measuring temperature

Extension. Work with a partner and test each other. For example: "*What do you call a chair with wheels in which an invalid can sit and move around?*"

Based on the **Dictionary of Medicine**, third edition
ISBN 1-901659-45-3
© Peter Collin Publishing Ltd

Chemistry

What are the names for the symbols of the chemical elements and compounds in the table below? Complete the 'name' column and connect each substance to the notes which refer to it. The first one has been done for you as an example.

	Symbol	Name	Notes
1.	Na	...**sodium** (e).......	(a) acid found in the gastric juices which helps the maceration of food
2.	Ca	....	(b) acid which forms cyanide
3.	Pb	....	(c) main alkaloid substance found in tobacco
4.	Ti	....	(d) used as a contrast when taking X-ray photographs of soft tissue
5.	Ba	....	(e) ~~the basic substance in salt~~
6.	Zn	....	(f) metallic element which is the basis of a radioactive isotope used to treat cancer
7.	Fe	....	(g) colourless gas with a sweet smell, used in combination with other gases as an anaesthetic in dentistry and surgery
8.	Co	....	(h) colourless gas which is present in air and essential to human life
9.	Cl	....	(i) one of the common non-metallic elements which is an essential component of living matter and organic chemical compounds
10.	He	....	(j) an essential part of the red pigment in red blood cells, found in liver and eggs
11.	S	....	(k) gas which combines with oxygen to form water
12.	Au	....	(l) heavy soft metallic element which is poisonous in compounds
13.	O	....	(m) very light gas used in combination with oxygen, especially to relieve asthma or sickness caused by decompression
14.	H	....	(n) light metallic element which does not corrode
15.	HCI	....	(o) gas which is the main component of air and an essential part of protein
16.	N	....	(p) metallic element which is the major component of bones and teeth
17.	HCN	....	(q) powerful greenish gas used to sterilize water
18.	C	....	(r) soft yellow-coloured poisonous metal used as a compound in various drugs and sometimes as a filling for teeth
19.	N_2O	....	(s) white metallic trace element
20.	$C_{10}H_{14}N_2$	....	(t) yellow non-metallic element found in some amino acids

Extension. Check the pronunciation of the 20 elements and compounds, then work with a partner to test each other: one person writes the symbol, while the other says the names.

Based on the **Dictionary of Medicine**, third edition
ISBN 1-901659-45-3
© Peter Collin Publishing Ltd

Anagrams 1

Solve the anagrams by reading the clues and putting the letters in order to form words. Write your answers in the grid to find the mystery word spelled by their initial letters.

1. Action of breathing.. RAEINOPRIST

2. Sensitivity to certain substances, such as pollen or dust which cause a physical reaction.. AEGLLRY

3. Girl child of a parent.. ADEGHRTU

4. Cut in a patient's body made by a surgeon using a scalpel............ CIIINNOS

5. Surgical intervention.. AEINOOPRT

6. Study of the process of ageing and the diseases of old people........ EGGLNOOORTY

7. Becoming worse after seeming to get better.............................. AEELPRS

8. Equipment used in a laboratory or hospital.............................. AAAPPRSTU

9. Give instructions for a patient to receive a certain dosage of a drug.. BCEEIPRRS

10. Place where sick or injured people are looked after...................... AHLIOPST

11. Physical or mental activity.. CEEEIRSX

12. Ability of a person not to get a disease.................................... ACEEINRSST

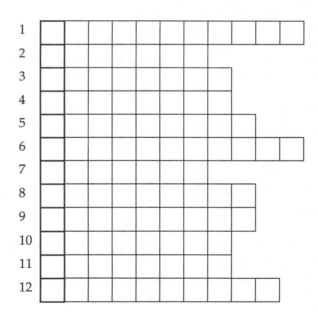

Mystery word: person specially trained to operate a machine to take X-ray photographs

---

Parts of the body crossword 1

All the answers in this crossword are parts of the body.

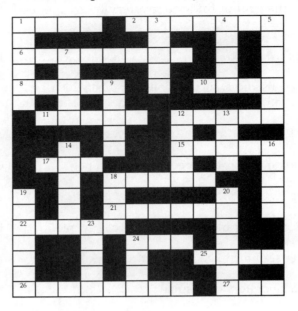

ACROSS

1   Joins the femur and the tibia (4)
2   The organ into which food passes after being swallowed and where the process of digestion continues (7)
6   The first part of the small intestine (8)
8   Hinged joint in the arm (5)
10 It grows on your head (4)
11 The upper chambers of 18 across (5)
12 Breathing organs (5)
15 They carry blood to 11 across (5)
17 Part of the body with which a person sees (3)
18 The organ which moves blood around your body (5)
21 Cell in the nervous system which transmits impulses (6)
22 An organ which secretes substances which act elsewhere in the body (5)
24 A substance which stores energy (3)
25 Tissue which forms the outside surface of the body (4)
26 Type of nerve ending (8)
27 For hearing with (3)

DOWN

1   It cleans your blood (6)
3   Main part of the body, without the arms, legs and head (5)
4   A major artery (5)
5   Connected to 8 across, funnily enough (7)
7   Eye socket (5)
9   Narrow part of the body below the chest and above the buttocks (5)
12 The major detoxicating organ (5)
13 Hard growth which forms on the top surface at the end of each finger and toe (4)
14 Cheekbone (6)
16 Protects the brain (5)
18 At the end of your arm (4)
19 The throat or neck, major artery (7)
20 Backs of the joints on a person's hand (7)
23 Bundle of fibres which take impulses from one part of the body to another (5)
24 End part of the leg on which a person stands (4)

Based on the **Dictionary of Medicine**, third edition
ISBN 1-901659-45-3
© Peter Collin Publishing Ltd

Communicative crossword 1 sheet A

This crossword is not complete: you have only half the words. The other half are on sheet B. Check that you know the words in your crossword. Then work with a partner who has sheet B to complete the two crosswords. Follow these three rules:

1. Speak only in English.

2. Don't say the word in the crossword.

3. Don't show your crossword to your partner.

"What's one across?"
→ across, ↓ down

Based on the **Dictionary of Medicine**, third edition
ISBN 1-901659-45-3
© Peter Collin Publishing Ltd

Communicative crossword 1   sheet B

This crossword is not complete: you have only half the words. The other half are on sheet A. Check that you know the words in your crossword. Then work with a partner who has sheet A to complete the two crosswords. Follow these three rules:

1. Speak only in English.

2. Don't say the word in the crossword.

3. Don't show your crossword to your partner.

> *"What's one across?"*
> → across, ↓ down

Based on the **Dictionary of Medicine**, third edition
ISBN 1-901659-45-3
© Peter Collin Publishing Ltd

Anagrams 2

Solve the anagrams by reading the clues and putting the letters in order to form words.
Write your answers in the grid to find the mystery word spelled by their initial letters.

1. Main part of the brain.. BCEEMRRU

2. Value calculated by adding together several quantities and dividing the total by the number of quantities.................. AAEEGRV

3. Effect produced by a stimulus.................................... ACEINORT

4. Way of acting.. ABEHIORUV

5. To notice or to see something and understand it.............. BEEORSV

6. Spasm causing sudden inhalation followed by closure of the glottis which makes a characteristic sound.................. CCHIPU

7. Reflex action when tired or sleepy............................... ANWY

8. To become worse.. ADEEIORRTTE

9. Reducing strain or stress.. AAEILNORTX

10. Not asleep.. AAEKW

11. Operating room.. AEEHRTT

12. Works well.. CEEFFIINT

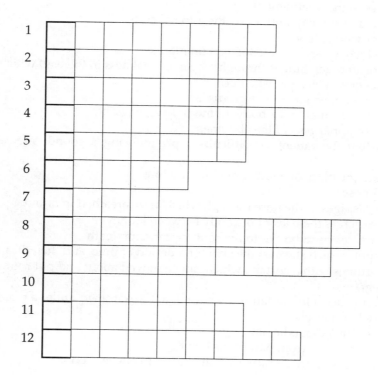

Mystery word: found in sugar and starch, and provides the body with energy

Based on the **Dictionary of Medicine**, third edition
ISBN 1-901659-45-3
© Peter Collin Publishing Ltd

Word search

Find the 28 medical terms and expressions hidden in the letters below; 14 read across and 14 read down. The first word has been found for you as an example. The clues listed beneath will help you to find all of the words.

P	A	T	H	O	L	O	G	I	S	T	W
E	C	N	O	S	T	R	I	L	P	R	O
N	L	S	C	R	E	E	N	I	O	I	M
D	I	M	M	U	N	E	A	V	T	C	B
E	N	B	C	S	L	I	D	E	W	E	T
M	I	L	B	E	D	S	O	R	E	P	H
I	C	O	R	T	I	S	O	N	E	S	E
C	H	C	P	A	N	C	R	E	A	S	R
D	O	U	E	T	A	P	A	A	G	T	N
F	S	M	L	I	S	P	S	S	E	A	I
A	T	O	N	Y	A	G	H	E	H	K	A
I	R	O	N	A	L	L	E	R	G	E	N

1. Number of years that a person has lived
2. Substance which produces hypersensitivity
3. Lack of tone or tension in the muscles
4. Decubitus ulcer
5. Small hospital or department in a large hospital which deals only with walking patients or which specializes in the treatment of certain conditions
6. Hormone secreted in small quantities by the adrenal cortex
7. To make (pain or worry) less
8. (Any disease) which is very common in certain places
9. Condition where an organ bulges through a hole or weakness in the wall which surrounds it
10. Person or animal on which a parasite lives
11. Protected against an infection or allergic disease
12. Chemical element essential to the body, found in liver, eggs, etc.
13. Large gland in the upper part of the abdomen
14. Speech defect where the patient has difficulty in pronouncing 's' sounds and replaces them with 'th'
15. Doctor who takes the place of another doctor for a time
16. Referring to the nose
17. One of the two passages in the nose through which air is breathed in or out
18. Gland which lies across the back of the body between kidneys
19. Doctor who examines dead bodies to find out the cause of death
20. Mass of small spots which stays on the skin for a period of time, and then disappears
21. Light wall, sometimes with a curtain, which can be moved about and put round a bed to shield the patient
22. Piece of glass, on which a tissue sample is placed, to be examined under a microscope
23. Small round mark or pimple
24. To swallow or to drink (a medicine)
25. To remove or drain liquid from part of the body
26. Muscle formed of three parts, which are joined to form one tendon
27. Not dry
28. Uterus

Based on the **Dictionary of Medicine**, third edition
ISBN 1-901659-45-3
© Peter Collin Publishing Ltd

Communicative crossword 2   sheet A

This crossword is not complete: you have only half the words. The other half are on sheet B. Check that you know the words in your crossword. Then work with a partner who has sheet B to complete the two crosswords. Follow these three rules:

1. Speak only in English.

2. Don't say the word in the crossword.

3. Don't show your crossword to your partner.

> *"What's one across?"*
> → across, ↓ down

Communicative crossword 2   sheet B

This crossword is not complete: you have only half the words. The other half are on sheet A. Check that you know the words in your crossword. Then work with a partner who has sheet A to complete the two crosswords. Follow these three rules:

1. Speak only in English.

2. Don't say the word in the crossword.

3. Don't show your crossword to your partner.

> "What's one across?"
> → across, ↓ down

Based on the **Dictionary of Medicine**, third edition
ISBN 1-901659-45-3
© Peter Collin Publishing Ltd

Parts of the body crossword 2

All the answers to this crossword are parts of the body.

ACROSS

1   Ligament (5)
4   One of the calcified pieces of connective tissue which make 1 down (4)
5   Organ used for hearing (3)
8   Sight, hearing, smell, taste and touch (6)
11 It connects your foot to your leg (5)
13 Thorax (5)
14 Other side to the front (4)
16 Egg-producing organ (5)
20 Clavicle (10)
21 One of twenty-four inside 13 across
23 Plural of foot (4)

DOWN

1   All the bones which make up a body (8)
2   Joint between the hand and the forearm (5)
3   Branch of a nerve, artery or vein (5)
4   Encephalon (5)
6   Inside layer of the eye which is sensitive to light (6)
7   In the middle of your face (4)
9   Cavity inside the body, including the cavities inside the head behind the cheekbone, forehead and nose (5)
10 Main muscle in 13 across
12 Part of the body which joins the head to the body (4)
14 Air passage from the trachea to the lungs (8)
15 Human tail, at the end of the backbone (6)
17 One of two muscles in the top part of the back which moves the shoulder blades (8)
18 Soft, fat flesh (4)
19 Wall between two parts of an organ (6)
21 Radix, point from which a limb grows (4)
22 One of ten found on 23 across (3)

Based on the **Dictionary of Medicine**, third edition
ISBN 1-901659-45-3
© Peter Collin Publishing Ltd

Gap fill crossword

Complete the crossword with the missing words from the sentences.

ACROSS

1. He _____ a new type of catheter. (8)
5. Blood _____ were taken from all the _____ staff in the hospital. (7)
7. There is a _____ of names in alphabetical order. (4)
8. She must have a cold - her _____ is running. (4)
9. We will _____ the operating theatre with the latest scanning devices. (5)
10. Fear of snakes is a common _____. (6)
13. Sugar is a source of _____ . (6)
14. The doctor _____ the patient's broken arm. (3)
16. When she cut her finger it _____. (4)
17. He breathed in the smoke from the fire and it made him _____. (5)
18. He went to see an _____ specialist about his deafness. (3)
19. Anorexic patients may become _____ and may need hospitalization. (9)
24. Can I make an _____ to see Dr Jones? (11)
26. The box is so heavy she can't _____ it off the floor. (4)
27. He became hysterical and had to be put under _____. (8)

DOWN

1. The catheter is _____ into the passage. (8)
2. How can you afford this _____ treatment? (9)
3. She gave _____ to twins. (5)
4. The surgeon was able to move the organ back to its _____ position. (8)
6. The doctor put her to _____ with a powerful narcotic. (5)
11. The patient suffers from an allergic _____ to oranges. (8)
12. Her _____ rate was very irregular. (5)
14. The lining of the uterus is _____ during menstruation. (4)
15. When you add the reagent, the solution will _____ blue. (4).
20. We have _____ out the extent of the tumour. (6)
21. The drug begins acting after a very short _____. (4)
22. There were two hundred _____ of cholera in the recent outbreak. (5)
23. The clinic has a _____ of 100. (5)
25. The _____ is the ratio of a person's mental age, given by an intelligent test, to the person's actual age. (2)

Based on the **Dictionary of Medicine**, third edition
ISBN 1-901659-45-3
© Peter Collin Publishing Ltd

Communicative crossword 3   sheet A

This crossword is not complete: you have only half the words. The other half are on sheet B. Check that you know the words in your crossword. Then work with a partner who has sheet B to complete the two crosswords. Follow these three rules:

1. Speak only in English.

2. Don't say the word in the crossword.

3. Don't show your crossword to your partner.

> *"What's one across?"*
> → across, ↓ down

Based on the **Dictionary of Medicine**, third edition
ISBN 1-901659-45-3
© Peter Collin Publishing Ltd

Communicative crossword 3   sheet B

This crossword is not complete: you have only half the words. The other half are on sheet A. Check that you know the words in your crossword. Then work with a partner who has sheet A to complete the two crosswords. Follow these three rules:

1. Speak only in English.

2. Don't say the word in the crossword.

3. Don't show your crossword to your partner.

> *"What's one across?"*
> → across, ↓ down

Based on the **Dictionary of Medicine**, third edition
ISBN 1-901659-45-3
© Peter Collin Publishing Ltd

Quiz

How many of these questions can you answer?

1. Name four sources of Vitamin D.

2. Complete the following sentence. "In human anatomy, the hand has a dorsal and a palmar surface, and the foot a dorsal and a _____ surface."

3. What is the difference between myopia and hypermetropia?

4. Which of the following substances are poisonous?
   - arsenic
   - cyanide
   - fructose
   - glucose
   - polyunsaturated fat
   - starch
   - strychnine

5. Fill the gaps in the sentence with the correct numbers.
   "Permanent teeth, otherwise known as adult teeth, are formed of eight incisors, _____ canines, _____ premolars and _____ molars."

6. What is the term for a doctor who manages the budget of money provided for his/her practice by the National Health Service, deciding how much money to allocate to such items as the purchase of hospital services, equipment and drugs, staff wages, maintenance of premises, etc.?

7. If a patient is living at home and going to a hospital for treatment, is he/she classed as an "inpatient" or an "outpatient"?

8. What is the child's term for the stomach or abdomen?

9. Are the following statements true or false?

   [T / F] Blood is formed of red and white corpuscles, platelets and plasma.
   [T / F] The liver maintains the circulation of the blood around the body by its pumping action.
   [T / F] A mastectomy is a surgical operation to deliver a baby by cutting through the abdominal wall into the uterus.

10. What is the normal average human body temperature?

11. To which part of the body do words beginning with "gastr-" refer

12. Formerly, burns were classified by degrees (first-degree burn and second-degree burn). The modern classification is into two categories. What are these categories?

Extension. Work with a partner and write a medical knowledge quiz. Make sure you know the answers. Then ask the questions to another pair of students in the class.

Based on the **Dictionary of Medicine**, third edition
ISBN 1-901659-45-3
© Peter Collin Publishing Ltd

Peter Collin Publishing
Vocabulary Record Sheet

WORD	CLASS	NOTES Translation or definition, example...

Based on the **Dictionary of Medicine**, third edition
ISBN 1-901659-45-3

Answer key

Word-building

Word association 1: missing links *(p.1)*
1. body
2. pain
3. bone
4. muscle
5. eye
6. cell

Word formation: nouns *(p.2)*
Exercise 1.
1. diagnosis   2. examination   3. prescription
4. suffering   5. operation   6. cure
7. recovery   8. analysis   9. infection
10. experience   11. replacement
12. degeneration   13. referral   14. excess
15. withdrawal

Exercise 2.
1. My diagnosis was that the patient had a heart condition.
2. I made a full examination of the patient.
3. I wrote a prescription for a course of antibiotics.
4. He experienced very little suffering.
5. The operation was performed immediately.
6. There is no cure for this disease.
7. He has made a full recovery.
8. The lab made an analysis of the blood sample.
9. We found an infection in the tissue.
10. He has six years' tropical work experience.
11. The patient was given a hip replacement.
12. There has been a degeneration in his condition.
13. The patient was given a referral to a specialist.
14. There was an excess of sugar in the blood sample.
15. This is the time for the withdrawal of the drugs treatment.

Two-word expressions *(p.3)*

1. heart attack   2. general anaesthetic
3. bone marrow   4. surgical intervention
5. milk teeth   6. plastic surgery
7. brain death   8. bedside manner
9. allergic reaction   10. clinical trial
11. malignant tumour
12. general practitioner   13. circadian rhythm
14. digestive system   15. balanced diet

Plural formation *(p.4)*
1. strata   2. feet   3. fibulae   4. glomeruli
5. abscesses   6. joints   7. bullae   8. testes
9. septa   10. fossae   11. crises
12. humeri   13. syringes   14. acetabula
15. larvae   16. chordae   17. varices
18. fungi   19. ganglia   20. villi
21. atria   22. pontes   23. ova   24. bouts
25. cortices

Word formation: adjectives *(p.5)*
1. The surgeons operated to repair the patient's *defective* heart valve.
2. His diet is calcium-*deficient*.
3. She is physically *dependent* on amphetamines.
4. The doctor noted an *excessive* amount of bile in the patient's blood.
5. A *hypoglycaemic* attack can be prevented by eating glucose or a lump of sugar when feeling faint.
6. The vaccine should make you *immune* to tuberculosis.
7. They have periods when they are completely *inactive*.
8. His foot is so *painful* that he can hardly walk.
9. I suffered *spinal* injuries in the crash.
10. She complained of *stiff* joints.

Word association 2: partnerships *(p.6)*
Exercise 1.
1. administer a drug
2. analyse a sample
3. arrange an appointment
4. burp a baby
5. catch a cold
6. detect an improvement
7. discontinue the treatment
8. ease the pain
9. fold your arms
10. prescribe antibiotics

Exercise 2.
1. The doctor will *administer a drug* to the patient.
2. She was *prescribed antibiotics*.
3. As soon as the patient reported sever side-effects, the doctor *discontinued the treatment*.
4. I've *caught a cold* from one of my colleagues at work.
5. The laboratory *analysed a sample* of the food and found traces of bacteria.
6. He sat down and *folded his arms*.

7. I would like to *arrange an appointment* with the dental hygienist for 10.00am tomorrow.
8. She had an injection to *ease the pain* in her leg.
9. The health visitor advised the new parents to *burp the baby* after feeding.
10. The nurses *detected an improvement* in the patient's condition.

Opposites 1: prefixes (p.7)

Exercise 1.

il-
1. illegal

im-
1. immoveable
2. impalpable
3. impure

in-
1. inactive
2. inadequate
3. incapable
4. incompatible
5. incomplete
6. incorrect
7. incurable
8. indirect
9. infertile
10. insanitary
11. insoluble

ir-
irreducible
irregular

un-
1. unboiled
2. unconscious
3. unfit
4. unhealthy
5. unhygienic
6. unpasteurized
7. unqualified
8. unstable
9. unwell

Exercise 2.
1. unconscious   2. unwell   3. incapable
4. unhealthy   5. irregular   6. unfit
7. unpasteurized   8. insanitary   9. unstable
10. incurable

Word formation: verbs (p.8)

Exercise 1.
1. abuse   2. admit   3. bandage
4. breathe   5. castrate   6. consult
7. convalesce   8. convert   9. fertilize
10. immunize   11. implant   12. insure
13. macerate   14. manage   15. occur
16. perspire   17. prepare   18. provide
19. reabsorb   20. regenerate   21. register
22. regurgitate   23. rehabilitate
24. reproduce   25. resuscitate   26. sedate
27. stammer   28. stitch   29. suppress
30. sweat

Word association 3: mind maps (p.9)

Exercise 1.
1. operating theatre   2. ODA
3. A&E department   4. major surgery
5. surgeon   6. local anaesthetic
7. consultant   8. heart surgery   9. scrub up
10. surgery

Parts of Speech

Nouns (p.10)
1. intolerance   2. paroxysms   3. overdose
4. surgery   5. programme   6. recurrence
7. tendency   8. examination   9. injection
10. exercise   11. ambulance   12. intake
13. biopsy   14. consent   15. whisper
16. effort   17. excess   18. accident
19. Vaccination   20. rash

Adjectives 1 (p.11)
1. safe   2. poisonous   3. compatible
4. inoperable   5. left-handed   6. inborn
7. inadequate   8. inactive   9. severe
10. confused   11. motionless   12. hygienic
13. predisposed   14. bitter   15. delicate
16. insanitary   17. highly strung
18. regular   19. invisible   20. hoarse

Adjectives 2 (p.12)
1. lethal   2. crippled   3. persistent
4. subjective   5. infirm   6. inflamed
7. level   8. painful   9. viable   10. deaf
11. premature   12. exhausted   13. awkward
14. bedridden   15. lame   16. obsessive
17. tender   18. severed   19. depressed
20. forbidden

Verbs 1 (p.13)
a) diagnose   b) treat   c) cure   d) endanger
e) prescribe   f) specialize   g) suffer
h) operate   i) vaccinate   j) soothe   k) depend
l) suppress

Verbs 2 (p.14)
a) transfer   b) harm   c) penetrate
d) perforate   e) probe   f) save   g) lack
h) admit   i) prevent   j) respond   k) faint
l) perform

Verbs: past tense ~ regular verbs (p. 15)
1. received   2. strained   3. recovered
4. fainted   5. required   6. suffered
7. adapted   8. developed   9. fractured
10. reacted   11. weighed   12. prolonged
13. aggravated   14. examined   15. trembled

1. visit   2. overcame   3. rebuilt
4. undergone   5. experiencing   6. broke
7. measures   8. expelled   9. kicking
10. heal   11. burnt   12. controls
13. beating   14. bitten   15. progressing

Phrasal verbs (p. 17)

1. got over   2. looking after   3. picked up
4. drops off   5. knocked down
6. broke down   7. takes after   8. take off
9. bringing up   10. depends on   11. give up
12. knocked out   13. propped up
14. getting on   15. carry out

Verbs: active/passive (p.18)

1. An acceleration in the patient's pulse was noticed by the nurse.
2. He is being allowed by the consultant to watch the operation.
3. The tablets are sold by all chemists.
4. Appendicitis was diagnosed by the doctor.
5. The injured man was comforted by the paramedics until the ambulance arrived.
6. The twins were delivered by the midwife.
7. An excess of hormones was being produced by the gland.
8. He was very well looked after in hospital.
9. The tissue was examined under the microscope.
10. I was given an unpleasant mixture to drink by the doctor.
11. The lotion cannot be taken orally.
12. The workers were poisoned by toxic fumes.
13. A rise in cases of whooping cough is being predicted by doctors.
14. The body's natural instinct to reject the transplanted tissue is suppressed by the drug.

Adverbs (p.19)

1. The bandage was *loosely* tied around her wrist.
2. *Mentally*, she is very advanced for her age.
3. If the patient sweats *excessively*, it may be necessary to cool his body with cold compresses.
4. The tumour is *awkwardly* placed and not easy to reach.
5. She manages all her patients very *efficiently*.
6. The relief team *urgently* requires more medical supplies.
7. This is a *mildly* antiseptic solution.
8. *Physically*, he is very weak, but his mind is still alert.
9. He became ill *immediately* after he came back from holiday.

Verbs: mixed tenses (p. 16)

10. The herb can be used *medicinally*.
11. He has been working as a doctor only for a *fairly* short time.
12. Her breathing was *severely* affected.

Prepositions (p.20)

1. The hospital has installed new apparatus ~~through~~∧ the physiotherapy department. *in*
2. Her lips were cracked ~~of~~∧ the cold.   *from*
3. The boy's little toe was crushed∧ the door. *by*
4. The tissue was examined ~~on~~∧ the microscope.   *under*
5. It is important that needles used ~~at~~∧ injections should be sterilized.   *for*
6. He is recovering from a bout∧ flu.   *of*
7. She was given ~~to~~ a pain-killing injection.
8. Some types of wool can irritate ~~to~~ the skin.
9. This report quotes the number of cases of cervical cancer ~~from~~ thousand patients tested.   *per*
10. The doctor put the patient to sleep with~~in~~ a strong narcotic.
11. She burnt her hand ~~at~~∧ the hot frying pan. *on*
12. We have no spare beds ~~on~~∧ the hospital at the moment.   *in*
13. He will have an operation to remove ~~of~~ an ingrowing toenail.
14. Please ensure that the patient takes ~~of~~ his medicine.

Pronunciation

Word stress 1 (p.21)

Group A: hospital   regular   exercise   alcohol   minimum   haemorrhage   operate   serious   theatre   painkillers   positive   medical   history
Group B: admitted   improvement   condition   develop   injection   equipment   allergic   reaction   prescription   infection   opinion
Group C: recommend   reassure   incomplete

Word stress 2 (p. 22)

Exercise 1.
1. complication   2. paralysis   3. emergency
4. respirator   5. operation   6. anaesthetic
7. disposable   8. intolerance   9. circulation
10. coordinate   11. experiment
12. malignancy   13. responsible
14. Analysis   15. compatible   16. saturated
17. demonstrated   18. dehydration
19. communicate   20. Penicillin

Exercise 2.

	A: ■□□	B: □■□	C: □□■
anaesthetic			X
analysis		X	
circulation			X
communicate		X	
compatible		X	
complication			X
coordinate		X	
dehydration			X
demonstrated	X		
disposable		X	
emergency		X	
experiment		X	
intolerance		X	
malignancy		X	
operation			X
paralysis		X	
penicillin			X
respirator	X		
responsible		X	
saturated	X		

Present simple (p.23)

Group A: coughs   helps   panics   beats
sleeps   wakes   counteracts   operates
regulates
Group B: breathes   examines   recommends
prescribes   relieves   suffers   controls
cures   kills
Group C: sneezes   reduces   catches   rises
analyses   diagnoses   relaxes   releases
increases

Past tense (p.24)

Group A: reduced   coughed   replaced
mixed   dressed   increased   noticed
dropped
Group B: diagnosed   improved   sneezed
prescribed   cured   probed   sterilized
Group C: vaccinated   consulted
recommended   prevented   operated
disinfected   treated   preceded

Vocabulary in Context

Good advice (p.25)

1. g)	8. f)
2. k)	9. n)
3. d)	10. b)
4. e)	11. a)
5. l)	12. i)
6. j)	13. c)
7. h)	14. m)

Multiple meanings (p.26)

1. patient   2. fit   3. degree   4. notice
5. turn   6. light   7. cold   8. degree
9. turn   10. patient   11. notice   12. fit
13. turn   14. fit   15. light   16. degree
17. fit   18. cold   19. light

Odd one out (p.27)

1. bleeding; the others are words which describe pains
2. liver; you have two of all the others
3. forearm; the others are all joints
4. face; the others are all specifically sense organs
5. patient; the others are all jobs
6. bandage; the others are all instruments
7. supination; the others are all connected to breathing
8. eyelids; the others are all eye conditions
9. relapse; the others all mean to return to normal after an illness
10. palm; the others are all parts of the eye
11. vertebral column; the others are all part of the ear
12. nickel; the others are all normally found in the body
13. wound; the others refer principally to damage to bones
14. metacarpal bone; the others are all in the skull
15. pancreas; the others deal with blood
16. taste; the others are all physical actions
17. hernia; the others relate to the liver
18. diabetes; the others are all part of the skin

Body parts - categories (p.28)

abdomen - torso	knuckle - hand
Achilles tendon - foot	lip - head
ankle - leg	nail - hand/foot
buttock - torso	navel - torso
calf - leg	neck - torso
chest - torso	nipple - torso
chin - head	nose - head
ear - head	palm - hand
elbow - arm	rib - torso
eye - head	scalp - head
eyebrow - head	shoulder - torso
eyelash - head	sole - foot
eyelid - head	temple - head
finger - hand	thigh - leg
forearm - arm	thumb - hand
forehead - head	toe - foot
gum - head	tongue - head
hip - torso	tooth- head
knee - leg	wrist - arm

Opposites 2 (p.29)
Exercise 1.
1. front   2. chronic   3. alive   4. deteriorate
5. ill   6. closed   7. minor   8. increase
9. rough   10. malignant
Exercise 2.
1. acute   2. increase   3. improve   4. back
5. rough   6. malignant   7. open   8. dead
9. healthy   10. major

Abbreviations (p.30)
1. A & E: Accident & Emergency
2. AIDS: Acquired Immunodeficiency Syndrome
3. BMR: Basal Metabolic Rate
4. CAT: Computerized Axial Tomography
5. CHD: Coronary Heart Disease
6. D & V: Diarrhoea & Vomiting
7. DOA: Dead On Arrival
8. GP: General Practitioner
9. HAV: Hepatitis A Virus
10. HIV: Human Immunodeficiency Virus
11. MD: Doctor of Medicine
12. OTC: Over The Counter
13. PM: Post Mortem
14. PMA: Progressive Muscular Atrophy
15. PMT: Premenstrual Tension
16. RQ: Respiratory Quotient
17. RSI: Repetitive Strain Injury
18. SAD: Seasonal Affective Disorder
19. SIDS: Sudden Infant Death Syndrome
20. STD: Sexually Transmitted Disease
21. TB: Tuberculosis
22. TBI: Total Body Irradiation
23. UV: Ultraviolet
24. VDH: Valvular Disease of the Heart
25. WHO: World Health Organization

Symptoms & common illnesses 1 (p.31)
1. influenza   2. rubella   3. coryza
4. varicella   5. rubeola
6. infectious parotitis   7. pertussis
8. allergic rhinitis

Symptoms & common illnesses 2 (p.32)
Exercise 1.
1. Chickenpox is the same as varicella
2. A cold is the same as coryza
3. The flu is the same as influenza
4. German measles is the same as rubella
5. Hay fever is the same as allergic rhinitis
6. Measles is the same as rubeola
7. Mumps is the same as infectious parotitis
8. Whooping cough is the same as pertussis
Exercise 2.
1. hay fever   2. German measles
3. whooping cough   4. flu   5. mumps
6. chickenpox

Diagnosis (p.33)
1. epilepsy   2. gangrene   3. cataracts
4. Parkinson's disease   5. tuberculosis
6. cystic fibrosis   7. cholera   8. diphtheria
9. cerebral palsy   10. gastroenteritis

How it works (p.34)
1. d)	10. h)
2. k)	11. p)
3. g)	12. q)
4. m)	13. c)
5. r)	14. o)
6. a)	15. l)
7. b)	16. j)
8. f)	17. i)
9. n)	18. e)

Instruments and equipment (p.35)
1. wheelchair   2. scalpel   3. probe
4. forceps   5. curette   6. pipette
7. tourniquet   8. hook   9. drain   10. gag
11. syringe   12. catheter   13. bandage
14. sling   15. stretcher   16. splint
17. stethoscope   18. thermometer

Chemistry (p.36)
1. Na, sodium, (e) the basic substance in salt
2. Ca, calcium, (p) metallic element which is the major component of bones and teeth
3. Pb, lead, (l) heavy soft metallic element which is poisonous in compounds
4. Ti, titanium, (n) light metallic element which does not corrode
5. Ba, barium, (d) used as a contrast when taking X-ray photographs of soft tissue
6. Zn, zinc, (s) white metallic trace element
7. Fe, iron, (j) an essential part of the red pigment in blood cells, found in liver & eggs
8. Co, cobalt, (f) metallic element which is the basis of a radioactive isotope used to treat cancer
9. Cl, chlorine, (q) powerful greenish gas used to sterilize water
10. He, helium, (m) very light gas used in combination with oxygen, especially to relieve asthma
11. S, sulphur, (t) yellow non-metallic element found in some amino acids
12. Au, gold, (r) soft yellow-coloured precious metal, used as a compound in various drugs and sometimes as a filling for teeth
13. O, oxygen, (h) colourless gas which is present in air and essential to human life
14. H, hydrogen, (k) gas which combines with oxygen to form water
15. HCl, hydrochloric acid, (a) acid found in the gastric juices which helps the maceration of food

16. N, nitrogen, (o) gas which is the main component of air and an essential part of protein
17. HCN, hydrocyanic acid, (b) acid which forms cyanide
18. C, carbon, (i) one of the common non-metallic elements which is an essential component of living matter and organic chemical compounds
19. N_2O, nitrous oxide, (g) colourless gas with a sweet smell, used in combination with other gases as an anaesthetic in dentistry and surgery
20. $C_{10}H_{14}N_2$, nicotine, (c) main alkaloid substance found in tobacco

Puzzles & Quizzes

Anagrams 1 (*p.37*)
1. Respiration
2. Allergy
3. Daughter
4. Incision
5. Operation
6. Gerontology
7. Relapse
8. Apparatus
9. Prescribe
10. Hospital
11. Exercise
12. Resistance

Anagrams 2 (*p.41*)
1. Cerebrum
2. Average
3. Reaction
4. Behaviour
5. Observe
6. Hiccup
7. Yawn
8. Deteriorate
9. Relaxation
10. Awake
11. Theatre
12. Efficient

Word search (*p.42*)

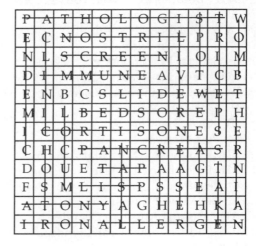

Parts of the body crossword 1 (*p.38*)

¹K	N	E	E		²S	³T	O	M	⁴A	C	⁵H
I						R			O		U
⁶D	U	⁷O	D	E	N	U	M		R		M
N		R				N			T		E
⁸E	L	B	O	⁹W		K		¹⁰H	A	I	R
Y		I		A					R		U
	¹¹A	T	R	I	A		¹²U	¹³N	G	S	
		S		T			I	A			
	¹⁴Z		T			¹⁵V	E	I	N	¹⁶S	
	¹⁷E	Y	E				E	L		K	
	G				¹⁸H	E	A	R	T	U	
¹⁹J		O			A			²⁰K		L	
U		M		²¹N	E	U	R	O	N	L	
²²G	L	A	²³N	D				U			
U		E			²⁴F	A	T				
L		R		O				²⁵S	K	I	N
A		V		O				L			
²⁶R	E	C	E	P	T	O	R		²⁷E	A	R

Parts of the body crossword 2 (*p.45*)

¹S	I	N	E	²W		³R		⁴B	O	N	E
K				R		A		R			
⁵E	A	⁶R		I		M		A			⁷N
L		E		S		U		I			O
E		T		T		⁸S	E	N	⁹S	E	S
T		I							I		E
O		N					¹⁰P		N		
N		¹¹A	¹²N	K	L	E			U		
			E				¹³C	H	E	S	T
			C				T				
¹⁴B	A	¹⁵C	K			¹⁶O	V	A	¹⁷R	Y	
R		O			¹⁸F		R		H		¹⁹S
O		²⁰C	O	L	L	A	R	B	O	N	E
N		C		A		L			M		P
C		Y		B				²¹R	I	B	T
H		X				²²T		O			U
U						O		O		I	M
S			²³F	E	E	T		D			

Gap fill crossword (p.46)

1I	N	V	2E	N	T	E	D			3B		4O
N			X							I		R
5S	A	M	P	L	E		6S			R		I
E			E			7L	I	S	T			G
R			8N	O	S	E	E		H			I
T			S			E						N
9E	Q	U	I	P		10P	H	O	B	I	A	
D			V		11R							L
	12P		13E	N	E	R	G	Y				
	U			A				14S	E	15T		
16B	L	E	D		17C	O	U	G	H		U	
	S			T					18E	A	R	
	19E	20M	A	C	I	A	21T	E	D		N	
22C		A			O		I			23S		
24A	P	P	O	25I	N	T	M	E	N	T		
S		P		Q			E			A		
E		E						26L	I	F	T	
27S	E	D	A	T	I	O	N			F		

SPECIALIST DICTIONARIES

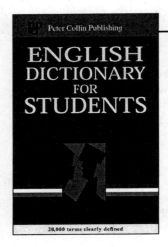

ENGLISH DICTIONARY FOR STUDENTS

A new general English dictionary written for intermediate to upper-intermediate level students. The Dictionary includes up-to-date coverage of English with over 20,000 terms, each clearly defined using a limited vocabulary of just 1500 words. Includes vocabulary used in TOEFL, TOEIC, UCLES, SAT and similar English exams.

l written for learners of English
l covers British and American terms
l phonetic pronunciation
l example sentences and quotations show usage

    ISBN 1-901659-06-2 720pages paperback £9.95 / US$15.95

CHECK YOUR VOCABULARY FOR ENGLISH

A companion workbook of exercises, puzzles, crosswords and word games to test general English skills. Provides material suitable for students taking Cambridge First Certificate/C.A.E level exams.

    ISBN 1-901659-11-9 £5.95 / US$9.95

For full details on our complete range of dictionaries and workbooks, visit our web site: www.petercollin.com
or use the form below to request further information.

English Dictionaries

English Dictionary for Students	1-901659-06-2	❏
Accounting	0-948549-27-0	❏
Aeronautical English	1-901659-10-0	❏
Agriculture, 2nd ed	0-948549-78-5	❏
American Business	0-948549-11-4	❏
Automobile Engineering	0-948549-66-1	❏
Banking & Finance, 2nd ed	1-901659-30-5	❏
Business, 2nd ed	0-948549-51-3	❏
Computing, 3rd ed	1-901659-04-6	❏
Ecology & Environment, 3rd ed	0-948549-74-2	❏
Government & Politics, 2nd ed	0-948549-89-0	❏
Hotel, Tourism, Catering Management	0-948549-40-8	❏
Human Resources & Personnel, 2ed	0-948549-79-3	❏
Information Technology, 2nd ed	0-948549-88-2	❏
Law, 3rd ed	1-901659-45-3	❏
Library & Information Management	0-948549-68-8	❏
Marketing, 2nd ed	0-948549-73-4	❏
Medicine, 3rd ed	1-901659-43-7	❏
Military Terms	1-901659-24-0	❏
Printing & Publishing, 2nd ed	0-948549-99-8	❏
Science & Technology	0-948549-67-X	❏

Vocabulary Workbooks

Banking & Finance	0-948549-96-3	❏
Business, 2nd ed	1-901659-27-5	❏
Computing, 2nd ed	1-901659-28-3	❏
Colloquial English	0-948549-97-1	❏
English for Students	1-901659-11-9	❏
English for Academic Purposes	1-901659-53-4	❏
Hotels, Tourism, Catering	0-948549-75-0	❏
Law, 2nd ed	1-901659-21-6	❏
Marketing	1-901659-48-8	❏
Medicine, 2nd ed	1-901659-47-X	❏

Professional/General

Astronomy	0-948549-43-2	❏
Economics	0-948549-91-2	❏
Multimedia, 2nd ed	1-901659-01-1	❏
PC & the Internet, 2nd ed	1-901659-12-7	❏
Bradford Crossword Solver, 3rd ed	1-901659-03-8	❏

Bilingual Dictionaries

French-English/English-French Dictionaries
German-English/English-German Dictionaries
Spanish-English/English-Spanish Dictionaries

Name: ....

Address: ....

....

....

....Postcode/Zip:.............................Country:.................................

Peter Collin Publishing Ltd
1 Cambridge Road
Teddington, TW11 8DT - UK
tel: +44 181 943 3386   fax: +44 181 943 1673   email: info@petercollin.com
web site: www.petercollin.com